focus on asia

Philippines

SCOTT BRODIE

CONTENTS

Philippines

LUZON

O Baguio

PHILIPPINE

SEA

O Tarlac

SOUTH

Quezon City

O
O MANILA

CHINA

SEA

MINDORO

O Calbayog

O Tacloban

PALAWAN

O Bacolod

NEGROS

O Cebu

O Puerto Princesa

SULU

O Cagayan de Oro

SEA

MINDANAO

O Davao

O Zamboanga

MALAYSIA

0   Kilometres   300

Copyright Trocadero Publishing

Introduction to the Philippines

The Philippines occupies a unique position in eastern Asia, being the only predominantly Christian nation in the region. Also, the combination of Malay heritage overlaid with Spanish-Catholic and later American influences has created a unique people. The Philippines is a place of great emotion, enthusiasm and passion.

While this makes it a very interesting country, there is less of the single-minded dedication to advancement and economic growth seen elsewhere in Asia. In the 1950s the Philippines was one of the most advanced countries in Asia, well ahead of Singapore, Malaysia, Thailand, Hong Kong, Taiwan and Korea. Now it lags behind all of them, thanks primarily to the appalling corruption of the Marcos era.

The nation faces many challenges today. One of the biggest is the divide between the Christian north and the Muslim minority in the Mindanao region. Another is the return of United States military personnel as advisers in the campaign against Muslim rebels. While Filipinos are enthusiastic about most things American, most draw the line at the possibility of foreign bases on their soil again.

A handsome government building from the American colonial era

SCOTT BRODIE

EUROPE

ASIA

NORTH AMERICA

AFRICA

PHILIPPINES

Pacific

Indian

SOUTH AMERICA

Ocean

Ocean

AUSTRALIA

Government structure

Country name
Pilipinas
(Philippines)
Official name
Republika ng Pilipinas
(Republic of the Philippines)
Government type
Republic
Capital
Manila
Head of state
President
Head of government
President
Cabinet
Appointed by the president
Legislative branch
Kongreso (Congress) comprising
Kapulungan Ng Mga Kinatawan
(House of Representatives) — lower house,
members elected for three-year term
Senado (Senate) —upper house,
members elected for six-year term
Administrative divisions
61 chartered cities
73 provinces
National holiday
Independence Day — 12 June
(independence from Spain)
Constitution
Latest version 11 February 1987
Legal system
Based on Anglo-American and Spanish law
Voting
18 years of age, universal, non-compulsory

American-style government with a president and a bicameral congress.

Today the legislature exists much as it did originally, with a House of Representatives (lower house) and a Senate (upper house). The lower house has 204 members, the upper house twenty-four. All are popularly elected — for three years in the case of the representatives, six years for the senators.

Originally presidents were elected for a four-year term, and could stand for re-election once. After the Marcos regime collapsed the constitution was revamped in 1987. It now

Except for the period of martial law under Ferdinand Marcos (1972–81), the Philippines has been one of the most democratic nations in Asia. In the run-up to independence in 1946 it adopted an

President Gloria Arroyo

NEWSPIX — JOEL NITO

Ferdinand and Imelda Marcos in the early 1980s, at the height of their power

PRESIDENTS OF THE REPUBLIC OF THE PHILIPPINES

1946–1948
Manuel Roxas
1948–1953
Elpidio Quirino
1953–1957
Ramón Magsaysay
1957–1961
Carlos García
1961–1965
Diosdad Macapagal
1965–1986
Ferdinand Marcos
1986–1992
Corazon Aquino
1992–1998
Fidel Ramos
1998–2001
Joseph Estrada
2001–
Gloria Macapagal Arroyo

allows for a six-year presidential term; however, the president cannot stand for re-election.

Philippine democracy can seem ferocious to outsiders. Free speech is carried to its greatest extremes as the legislature does battle with the office of the president. Newspaper commentators regularly attack the policies and personal behaviour of those in power.

Marcos

The recent history of the Philippines is inextricably linked to Ferdinand Edralin Marcos. Born in 1917, he originally trained as a lawyer before entering politics. From the start he used his official positions to enhance his personal wealth. He also claimed to have been a resistance hero during World War II, although there is no proof of this. Elected president in 1965, he invoked martial law to avoid having to leave office at the end of his second term, as required by the constitution. During his terms, Marcos and his cronies in business amassed vast wealth from corrupt activities, crippling the country's economy in the process. He was forced from office in 1986 by a popular uprising.

www.sources
www.gov.ph
Official Philippines government site

www.gov.ph/cat_foreignaffairs
Department of Foreign Affairs site

www.gov.ph/op
The president's official site

Transport

One of the thousands of jeepneys on the streets of the Philippines

Public transport

One aspect of Philippine public transport is world famous — the jeepney. About the size of a stretched four-wheel-drive vehicle, there is a driver's cab at the front and an enclosed area behind with long bench seats. Jeepneys operate like mini buses, on designated routes. Usually a jeepney is owned by a family, with brothers alternating the driving duties

There are no restrictions on how many jeepneys may operate on a route. Thus, busy main thoroughfares can be jammed with them. At designated stops people climb aboard for their journey, paying the driver a small fare.

Jeepneys originated in the years after World War II. When vast numbers of United States military jeeps became available for sale they were adapted to taxi duties. Before long manufacturers began building more elaborate versions. Jeepney owners often decorate their vehicles with elaborate paintwork, signs and ornaments

PHILIPPINES' HIGHWAYS

PAVED

UNPAVED

TOTAL
199 950 KM

In 1985 a single elevated light-rail track was constructed from Pasay to Caloocan in Manila. It was a project initiated by Imelda Marcos during her term as governor of Metro Manila. Unfortunately the viaduct on which it runs creates dark canyons in older districts such as Santa Cruz.

In the 1990s serious moves were made to reduce traffic congestion on Manila streets by expanding the light-rail network to around 135 kilometres of track. In 2001 the first of the new lines opened. It runs most of the length of Epifanio de los Santos Avenue (EDSA), the main highway linking the northern and southern ends of Manila. Other lines are under construction in Quezon City and elsewhere.

After jeepneys, buses are the most common form of transport in the Philippines. In Manila and all provincial cities and towns there are regular commuter bus services run by private companies. They compete with one another for passengers on all the main roads, causing traffic congestion at stops.

As many of these buses are old and poorly maintained, they are major contributors to air pollution. Also, the drivers of commuter buses are notorious for their erratic driving techniques.

Taxis are almost as common as jeepneys on Philippine streets. Usually small sedans, their standards vary — some are very shabby, others are smart and clean. Taxis are metered, but many drivers prefer negotiating a fixed fare, which is usually more than

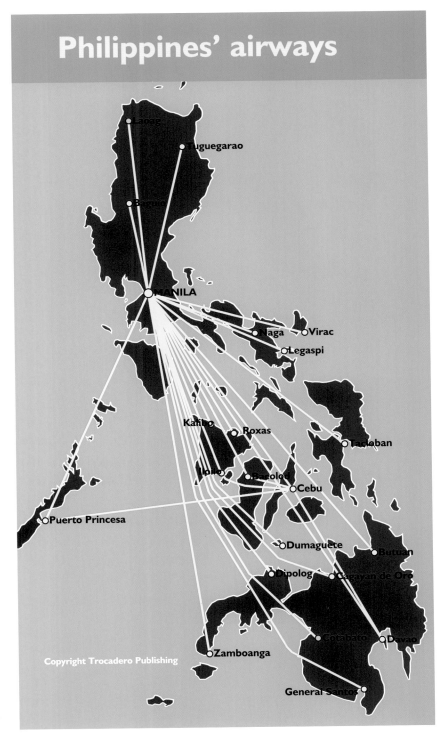

Philippines' airways

what the meter would show. Taxis are widely used because they are relatively cheap.

PHILIPPINES' MAIN PORTS AND HARBOURS

Batangas
Cagayan de Oro
Cebu
Davao
Guimaras Island
Iligan
Iloilo
Jolo
Legaspi
Manila
Masao
Puerto Princesa
San Fernando
Subic Bay / Olongopo
Zamboanga

Rail

Rail is not a major factor in Philippine transport. There are around 897 kilometres of narrow-gauge (1.067-metre) track, but only about fifty per cent is in use. The main track runs from Manila to southern Luzon, with several daily passenger services.

In addition to public railways, privately owned tramways haul harvested sugar cane to mills for processing. These are mostly found on the island of Negros where the sugar industry is dominant.

Road

With little in the way of railways, roads assume major importance. Car usage is high, partly because fuel prices are kept relatively low. The narrow streets of many cities and towns are heavily congested, not having been designed for modern-day vehicles.

In Manila a program of building freeways and overpasses has been going on for some years. This has alleviated some of the worst congestion. However, the overall standard of roads is poor, with many prone to flooding during heavy rain.

Long-distance buses are the most popular form of transport around the islands. Few Filipinos can afford air fares. Many bus companies operate routes from Manila to the provinces. At holiday times roads from the capital are jammed with buses as workers return to their families in the provinces.

Aviation

Being an archipelago, the Philippines relies heavily on aviation to maintain links for passengers and essential supplies. Philippine Airlines, Air Philippines and Cebu Air all operate regular domestic services to many parts of the country. Main

PHILIPPINES' SHIPPING FLEET

Bulk 149
Cargo 123
Chemical tanker 4
Combination bulk 10
Container 5
Liquefied gas 13
Livestock carrier 10
Passenger 4
Passenger/cargo 12
Petroleum tanker 42
Refrigerated cargo 21
Roll-on roll-off 17
Short-sea passenger 31
Specialised tanker 2
Vehicle carrier 16

A remarkably quiet Sunday on Roxas Boulevard, Manila — normally the roadway is jammed with traffic

trunk routes are served by larger jet aircraft; services to other centres are handled by smaller prop-jets.

During the Asian economic crisis of 1997–98, mounting debts forced Philippine Airlines to cease operations. However, with new owners and financing, it has since re-emerged as the country's main carrier. As well as domestic services, it flies regularly to North America, Australia, Europe and most parts of Asia.

Until recently Philippine airports have been fairly rudimentary affairs. Manila's Ninoy Aquino International Airport opened a new terminal building and upgraded domestic facilities in 1999. Further plans are under way to rebuild the rest of the airport to current international standards.

Shipping

The Philippines has a long maritime heritage. There are regular inter-island services, with large passenger ferries carrying people and cargo. The Philippines also offers a 'flag of convenience' service to shipowners from other countries, notably Japan. This enables owners to register vessels for lower costs than would be payable in their home countries.

Another aspect of Philippine maritime culture is the number of Filipinos serving as crew on ships around the world. This vast army of men leave their homes and families for months, sometimes years, manning everything from the finest luxury cruise liners to the worst cargo ships.

Communications

**PHILIPPINES'
TELEPHONE USAGE**

TOTAL POPULATION

TELEPHONE LINES INSTALLED

CELLULAR TELEPHONES IN USE

0 MILLIONS 20   40   60   80   100

The Philippines lags well behind other Asian countries in telecommunications. There are fewer than two million telephone lines in use for a country of more than eighty million people. Sometimes it takes years to have a telephone line installed, even in Manila. To supplement cable telephone services, eleven satellite earth stations have been built to improve domestic communications.

To overcome the lack of fixed-line telephones, many people have turned to mobile telephones. There are now more mobiles in use than fixed-line telephones. Filipinos are also among the world's largest users of text messaging services on their mobiles.

Radio and television are key sources of entertainment and information. More than 360 AM stations and 290 FM stations broadcast a wide range of programming. Much of it is musical or opinion, with outrageous program hosts providing lots of colour over the airwaves. Filipinos enjoy most Western music, as well as their own local variety. They are renowned singers and musicians.

Television is much like radio, with lots of home-grown programming interspersed among mainly American imports. Advertising content of television is very high. Very short bursts of programming separate the seemingly interminable commercial breaks.

The Philippines has one of the most vibrant newspaper publishing environments in Asia. Numerous daily newspapers, in both English and Pilipino, battle to present their versions of the day's news or gossip. There is no censorship on newspapers as occurs in other Asian countries. Thus, politicians are regular targets for virulent attacks from journalists and columnists.

Filipinos have a considerable reputation as talented computer programmers. The internet is very popular, even though the bulk of the population cannot afford a computer or even access to one. There are around half a million regular users and no government controls.

WWW.SOURCES

www.pldt.com.ph
Philippine Long Distance Telephone Company

www.asianinfo.org/asianinfo/
entertainment/tv/philippines.htm
Links to Philippine radio and television sites

www.newsdirectory.com/news/press/as/ph
Links to Philippine newspapers

Industry: primary and secondary

Terrible economic mismanagement in the Marcos era left the Philippines with major problems. Rampant corruption saw the country being shunned by foreign investors. Although this was gradually overcome during the Aquino and Ramos presidencies in the 1990s, the Philippines still lags behind other Asian nations.

Ultra-fertile volcanic soils and high rainfall have made agriculture a key part of the economy. Rice, sugar cane, corn and coconuts are the major

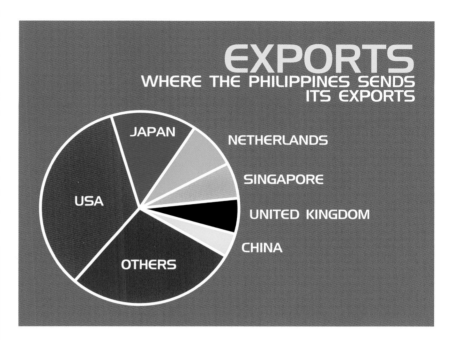

EXPORTS
WHERE THE PHILIPPINES SENDS ITS EXPORTS

JAPAN
NETHERLANDS
SINGAPORE
USA
UNITED KINGDOM
CHINA
OTHERS

PHILIPPINES' EXPORTS
US$38 billion
Main exports
electronic equipment, machinery, transport equipment, garments, coconut products, labour services

The Makati business district of Manila

SCOTT BRODIE

crops; bananas, coffee and hemp are also important. Intensive farming of pigs, poultry, goats and water buffalo also occurs. The seas around the islands provide a rich source of food,

Increasingly, manufacturing industries such as this vehicle plant are being set up in the Philippines

which is harvested in fish traps or from boats.

Natural resources are exploited in many regions. Fine-quality commercial timber is harvested and shipped to world markets. Mining is of growing importance, with nickel, zinc, copper, cobalt, gold, silver and iron ore extracted in large quantities. The Benguiat gold mines have been a source of wealth for decades. Substantial

PHILIPPINES' MAIN SECONDARY INDUSTRIES
textiles, pharmaceuticals, chemicals, wood products, food processing, electronics assembly, petroleum refining, fishing

reserves of oil were discovered in the seas around Palawan in recent years.

Although the growth in manufacturing has not been as great as hoped, considerable advances have been made. Most industry is concentrated in and around Manila. Of particular importance are electronics and associated

IMPORTS
WHERE THE PHILIPPINES' IMPORTS COME FROM

CHINA
TAIWAN
SINGAPORE
SOUTH KOREA
JAPAN
USA
OTHERS

Traps such as these are used throughout the Philippines to catch fish.

components, and assembly of electrical products. Motor cars and trucks are assembled, and chemicals and pharmaceuticals are key manufactures.

PHILIPPINES' IMPORTS
US$35 billion
Main imports
raw materials, intermediate goods, capital goods, consumer goods, fuels

PHILIPPINES' PRIMARY INDUSTRIES
rice, coconuts, corn, sugar cane, bananas, pineapples, mangoes, pork, eggs, beef, fish

www.sources
www.apmforum.com/columns/orientseas17.htm
History of the Philippines' sugar industry

www.philsol.nl/L-Mining.htm
Mining industries in the Philippines

www.census.gov.ph
Statistics on Philippine industries

Geography, environment and climate

The Philippines comprises more than 7000 islands, ranging from mere rocky outcrops to major land masses. Around 400 of these are inhabited. The eleven largest islands account for ninety-five per cent of the land area. The nation stretches 1850 kilometres from north to south and 1100 kilometres from east to west. It is mainly volcanic in origin, with substantial mountains found on most larger islands. Many volcanoes become active from time to time and earthquakes are common.

The Pasig River, which flows through Manila, is heavily polluted

SCOTT BRODIE

PHILIPPINES' LAND USE

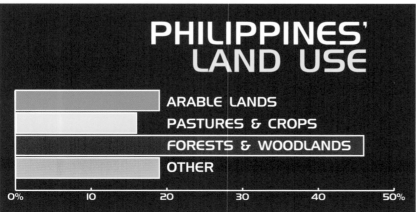

ARABLE LANDS
PASTURES & CROPS
FORESTS & WOODLANDS
OTHER

0%   10   20   30   40   50%

MANILA'S TEMPERATURE RANGE

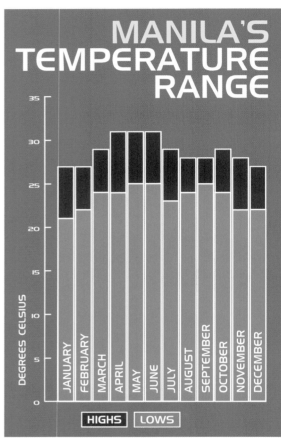

DEGREES CELSIUS

35
30
25
20
15
10
5
0

JANUARY FEBRUARY MARCH APRIL MAY JUNE JULY AUGUST SEPTEMBER OCTOBER NOVEMBER DECEMBER

HIGHS   LOWS

Completely within the tropical zone, the Philippine climate is dominated by the north-east monsoon (November–April) and the south-west monsoon (May–October). Lowland areas are hot and humid most of the year. Large cities such as Manila are particularly oppressive in the middle months of the year. As many as twenty destructive typhoons blow in

PHILIPPINES' SIZE
Total area
298 170 sq. km
Coastline 36 289 km
Border countries
none

THE PHILIPPINES' LARGEST ISLANDS
Luzon, Mindanao, Samar, Negros, Palawan, Panay, Mindoro, Leyte, Cebu, Bohol, Masbate

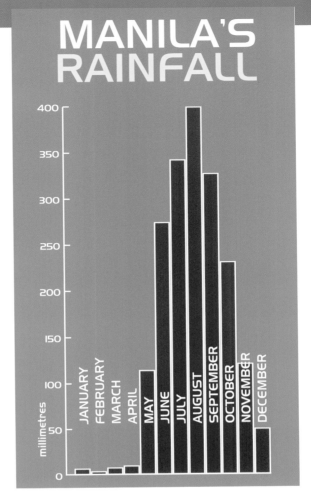

MANILA'S RAINFALL

millimetres

JANUARY
FEBRUARY
MARCH
APRIL
MAY
JUNE
JULY
AUGUST
SEPTEMBER
OCTOBER
NOVEMBER
DECEMBER

from the surrounding oceans each year. They bring strong winds and heavy rain, often causing widespread property damage.

The Philippines has some major environmental problems. In cities such as Manila, industrial and household waste is regularly discharged into streams. This has caused waterways to become chronically polluted. In rural areas, over-exploitation of timber resources has led to soil erosion. Pollution of waterways is increasingly affecting fish breeding grounds along the coast. Heavy motor vehicle usage contributes greatly to air pollution, notably in Manila.

PHILIPPINES' LOCATION
Latitude   13°N
Longitude 122°E

The crater of the Taal volcano, now a huge lake

SCOTT BRODIE

Peoples and daily life

PHILIPPINES'
POPULATION
TOTAL 82 850 000

AGED 0–14 YEARS
AGED 15–65 YEARS
AGED 65+ YEARS

0%   10   20   30%   40   50   60%

The large majority of Filipinos are descended from Malays who migrated to the islands thousands of years ago. The Philippines of today is a creation of European colonialism, rather than a homogeneous region with a single ethnic base. The national identity was forged only in the past 600 years. There are also peoples who want to

Filipinos are great readers, and the main cities and towns are well served by bookshops

PHILIPPINES'
ETHNIC MIX

MALAY

CHINESE
OTHERS

break away from the country. These are mostly found in the southern islands, where Islam is dominant.

A large number of Filipinos are bilingual or multilingual. The national language is Pilipino, which is based heavily on the Tagalog dialect. Apart from Tagalog, there are seven other major dialects spoken across the islands. Most educated Filipinos are also proficient in English. This is a result of the education system put in place during the American colonial period.

While Filipinos are fiercely proud of their culture and their country,

they do let a lot of American influences filter in. Fun-loving and passionate, they are also quick to anger when insulted or offended.

At first glance it appears the culture is very male-dominated. In fact, women are the backbone of the home and of the nation. They control the

Cinemas screening Philippine films

homes and play prominent roles in public and business life. Long before other Asian countries, the Philippines had women running companies and government departments. It has now had two women as head of state.

Hundreds of thousands of Filipinos, known as balikbayans, work outside their country. They journey to places such as Singapore, Malaysia, Hong Kong, Japan, Taiwan, the Middle East and elsewhere to work as domestic servants, labourers or ship crews. Fluency in English is one reason for their obtaining these jobs. Most work for a number of years, remitting wages back to their families.

of whom are national celebrities. Reading is also a popular pastime. Numerous large and small bookshops offer local and international publications at very low prices.

LANGUAGES

Official languages
Pilipino, English

Major dialects
Tagalog, Cebuano, Ilocan, Hiligaynon or Ilonggo, Bicol, Waray, Pampango, Pangasinense

Filipinos are very gregarious. They love to party and they enjoy the company of family and friends. Most are good singers and, even if they are not, are expected to perform at social functions. Eating out is popular, at Filipino restaurants or any of the many Asian and Western restaurants that dot the cities.

They are also great movie-goers, lapping up both Western-style and Philippine films. There is a large community of film stars in Manila, many

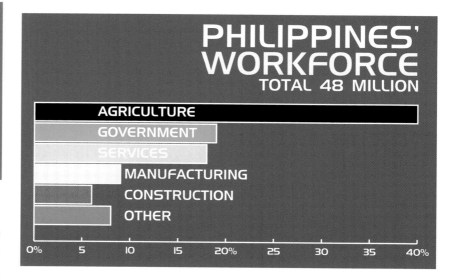

PHILIPPINES' WORKFORCE
TOTAL 48 MILLION

- AGRICULTURE
- GOVERNMENT
- SERVICES
- MANUFACTURING
- CONSTRUCTION
- OTHER

0% 5 10 15 20% 25 30 35 40%

www.sources

www.univie.ac.at/Voelkerkunde/apsis/aufi/ethno/ethnic.htm
Ethnic minorities in the Philippines

u2asean.com/phildir/entertainment.htm
Links to entertainment and leisure sites

www.filipinoheritage.com/traditions/tradition.htm
Philippine traditions and customs

Religion and beliefs

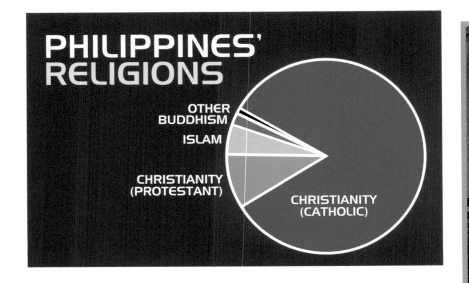

PHILIPPINES' RELIGIONS

OTHER
BUDDHISM
ISLAM
CHRISTIANITY
(PROTESTANT)
CHRISTIANITY
(CATHOLIC)

A typical Philippine Catholic church

Christianity was introduced to the Philippines by the Spanish in the late sixteenth century and quickly became the dominant faith of the islands. It effectively halted any further spread of Islam, which is entrenched in the Mindanao and Sulu regions. With the first Spanish colonial ships came groups of friars, who quickly began converting the peoples to Catholicism.

The Catholic Church plays an important role — its influence permeates all aspects of daily life. Church leaders such as Cardinal Jaime Sin are voices of morality and national identity, particularly in times of crisis. Around eighty per cent of the population is Catholic, with many of these attending Mass regularly.

The church's role in recent times has often been very positive, particularly in the overthrow of the Marcos regime. At other times it is a negative force, holding the country back. Most notable is the dogged refusal to sanction any form of birth control. Thus the population has been growing at a much greater rate than other nations, putting enormous pressure on space and resources.

www.sources

www.asianphilanthropy.org/countries/
philippines/religion.html
Details of religion in the Philippines

www.asianinfo.org/asianinfo/culture_society/
religion/philippines.htm
Links to sites about religions in the Philippines

www.filipinoheritage.com/religious/religion2.htm
Historical and current details on religions

Food and cuisine

Rice, or sometimes cassava, is the basic accompaniment to all Philippine meals. The cooking is a hybrid of local styles, interlaced with Malay, Spanish and Chinese influences. Spanish cooking has probably had the largest impact. The preferred eating utensils are the fork and spoon, with the spoon being used like a knife to break up pieces of food.

Fish of all types is immensely popular, with many varieties being harvested from local waters. Philippine food is milder than dishes of other Asian countries. Hot chillies and such ingredients are only favoured in southern regions. Coconut milk is highly favoured in the cooking of meats and vegetables and the creation of desserts.

Filipinos eat both at home and out. Meals can be purchased from street hawkers or eaten in a wide array of restaurants. These range from the simple and cheap to the most luxurious. Many serve a combination of Philippine and Western meals. Western-style foods are readily available from chains such as McDonalds, KFC, Wendy's, TGI Friday's and Tony Roma's, as well as the huge local Jolibee hamburger chain.

PHILIPPINE CUISINE

Sinigang
sour soup with seafood and vegetables

Adobo
stewed pork and chicken served with onions

Mechado
stew of beef, pork, potato, tomato and onions

Lechon
pork spit roast — essential on festive occasions

Lumpia
Philippines-style spring roll

Fresh Lumpia
chopped coconut, shrimps and pork wrapped in crepe-like pastry, served with garlic, sugar and soy sauce

Atchara
pickled papaya, spring onions, carrots and chilli

A food stall in Zamboanga

www.sources
www.filipinoheritage.com/food/basic_methods.htm
Philippine foods and cuisine

www.virginia.edu/~intcent/Docs/Cuisine/philippine.html
History and evolution of Philippine cuisine

www.barkada.de/nasud/cuisine.html
Eating habits, hospitality, what to eat

Arts and crafts

The Philippines has a rich history of arts and crafts. Hundreds of years ago theatrical traditions emerged with productions in villages for the locals. These tended to revolve around representations of the spirits, which were thought to control the seasons and the weather.

From the late 1500s Spanish influences crept into theatre and music. By the nineteenth century the zarzuela comic opera had many fans throughout the Philippines. Their emphasis on comedy, song and dance appealed greatly to the Filipino nature. Zarzuela were most often staged in conjunction with village fiestas.

There is a thriving film industry in the Philippines. The first movie cameras came to the islands in the late nineteenth century, and the first cinemas opened around the same time. Over the decades the industry has grown, catering to the desire of Filipinos to see their own people and stories on the screen. Today movie-making is big business and the stars are nationally known.

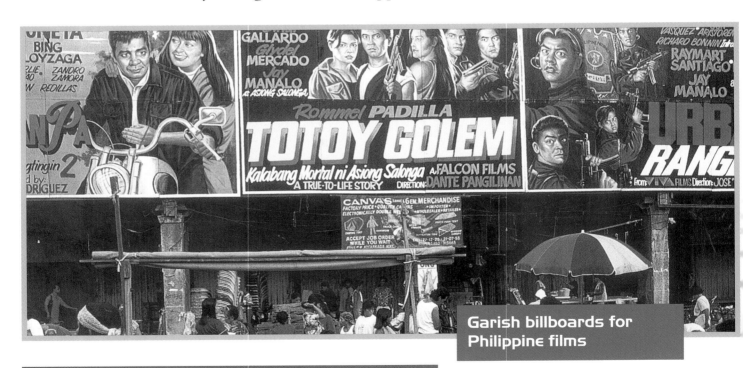

Garish billboards for Philippine films

www.sources

aedv.cs.tu-berlin.de/~brandeis/bukidmus.html
Traditional Philippine music

www.filipinoheritage.com/arts_crafts/arts.htm
Philippine arts and crafts

dmoz.org/Regional/Asia/Philippines/
Arts_and_Entertainment/Movies
Links to Philippine film sites

Literature of all kinds has always been very important. National hero José Rizal used novels to highlight the oppression of Spanish rule. As well as more intellectual writing there is a large industry in mass fiction, particularly romances featuring Filipino characters, written by locals.

History and politics

Early peoples

It is generally believed that peoples from Borneo, Malaya and Sumatra, known as the Negritos, migrated to the Philippine islands as much as 30 000 years ago. They probably used a land bridge that existed at the time. Most Filipinos are descended from proto-Malays who migrated from the Asian mainland. They were joined by another group from the Indonesian archipelago.

By AD 300 a distinct Filipino people was emerging. By the fourteenth century they had developed trade links and were active in mining, ship-building and weaving. Trade also developed 2500 years ago with the powerful kingdoms of Java and Sumatra, and 1000 years ago with China.

Islam arrives

The first culturally unifying movement was the arrival of Islam. Arab traders active in Indonesia landed on the southern islands. However, their teachings only caught on in a major way in the Mindanao and Sulu regions. The spread of Islam was effectively stymied by the arrival of Christianity.

Spain arrives

The Spanish beat the Portuguese to be the first Europeans to arrive in the Philippines. On 17 March 1521 the great explorer Ferdinand Magellan anchored his ships off the island of Homonhon, near Samar. He claimed the islands for the Spanish king, naming them Islas Filipinas after

The battle at Mactan, in which Magellan was killed

the infant Philip, heir to the throne. Soon afterwards Magellan was killed in a skirmish with warriors led by chief Lapu Lapu on Mactan Island.

Creating the colony

In 1564, sailing from New Spain (Mexico), Miguel López de Legaspi founded a settlement at what is now Cebu. Five years later, on the shores of a large bay on the island of Luzon, he established a settlement called Manila.

Legaspi secured the cooperation of the datus (chieftains). He guaranteed they would retain their status if they pledged allegiance to the Spanish throne.

The Philippines was an offshoot of Mexico, not a full Spanish colony in its own right. An all-powerful governor was based in Manila, supported by a small group of highly corrupt career civil servants.

SCOTT BRODIE

Christianity arrives

Legaspi had on board five Augustinian friars, who began converting the locals to Christianity. The residents were remarkably receptive to the message. After the Augustinians came the Dominicans, Jesuits and Franciscans. Through them Spanish culture permeated to most parts of the islands.

Feudalism

The colonists imposed a feudal system on the islands. The datus saw this as an excellent opportunity to consolidate their power. People who had worked their own plots for centuries now found themselves tied to a landlord.

Catholic control

Across the archipelago local priests acted as quasi-government officials. Loyal to the administration in Manila, they sent back regular reports and were eventually placed on the civil service payroll. Spain could never have retained control of the vast Philippine territory without them.

Commerce grows

Manila was also an important commercial centre. In 1601 it had trading links with China, India and the Indonesian archipelago. However, the real money was made in trade with Mexico.

All shipments, mainly high-quality silks, went to Mexico on government-owned ships called the Manila Galleons. On the return voyage they carried silver bullion as payment.

Continuing rebellion

Not everyone was happy about life under Spanish control. The most aggressive opponents were the Muslim peoples, known as the Moros, who conducted a guerrilla war against Spain until well into the nineteenth century. Particularly upsetting to the Moros was the wealth of the Catholic orders, which had been given vast tracts of land by the administration.

Effects of immigration

After the Mexican War of Independence in the nineteenth century, there was increased migration to the Philippines by Spaniards. Communities of mestizos (mixed bloods) developed. Relatively well educated, they became the elite of the native Filipinos.

Steady migration by Chinese over 200 years produced another cultural strain. Intermarriage between Chinese and Filipinos was common. Chinese-Filipinos, heavily involved in trade, lived mostly in the Binondo precinct of Manila.

Mestizo commerce

Mestizos began acquiring large areas of land in the eighteenth century. They converted the previously uninhabited island of Negros to sugar cane cultivation. They also did deals with local Catholic orders to lease land for rice cultivation. This was the foundation of the fabulously wealthy Filipino landowning families of today.

Growing rebellion

Mestizos also led moves for greater freedom from Spanish domination. In the 1880s, from their ranks emerged José P Rizal. A Chinese-Filipino scientist, he was educated in Spain and Germany. Outraged by the excesses of Spanish control, he published two novels: *Noli Me Tangere* (1886) and *El Filibusterismo* (1891). They detailed in fictional form everything he believed was wrong with Spanish colonialism.

In December 1896 the push for revolution peaked when forces led by Emilio Aguinaldo staged an uprising on Luzon. They achieved considerable success against the ill-prepared Spanish garrison. The administration, desperately looking for someone to blame, chose Rizal.

The Spanish authorities had arrested Rizal on his return from Europe in 1892. After the uprising he was hauled before a court on concocted charges of conspiracy with Aguinaldo. On 30 December 1896 Rizal was executed by firing squad.

The Americans

Cuba, Spain's major Caribbean colony, was swept by revolution in 1898. Seeing Cuba as within its sphere of influence, the United States declared war on Spain. On 1 May 1898 a United States Navy squadron, commanded by Commodore George Dewey, destroyed a ramshackle Spanish fleet in Manila Bay.

United States troops landed on the islands to clear out the Spanish. Aguinaldo returned from exile in Hong Kong to join forces with Dewey. American troops entered Manila in August 1898 to accept the Spanish garrison's surrender. Filipinos thought the time of liberation had come.

Colonial America

The Treaty of Paris in 1898 ended the Spanish–American War. Under its terms the United States annexed the former Spanish colonies of the Philippines, Guam and

José P Rizal

Emilio Aguinaldo

Puerto Rico. Aguinaldo and his followers were outraged. They had already declared the Philippines independent and established a provisional government. The Americans told Aguinaldo his supporters would be fired upon if they entered Manila.

Filipino–American War

When the independence movement refused to accept President William McKinlay's policy of 'benevolent assimilation' they were branded as insurrectionists. Aguinaldo's army became guerrilla fighters, taking to the mountains.

The United States government sent in a huge army to pacify the opponents. More than 600 000 Filipinos were massacred by United States forces. The capture of Aguinaldo in 1901 effectively ended large-scale resistance.

Consolidating power

A civil government under William H Taft introduced a number of positive developments. The most effective was the army of American teachers sent all over the archipelago to pass their expertise on to local teachers.

Taft negotiated the hand-over of the vast Catholic Church estates for US$7 million, but did little about land reform. The old feudal system was left in place to keep the mestizos on side. The United States needed their support to control the Philippines.

United States corporations invested little in the Philippines, but did benefit from low labour costs, particularly in agriculture. After 1909 all Philippine goods entered the United States without duties or taxes.

Hints of independence

In the United States a Democrat congress elected in 1913 increased the powers of the Philippine lower house and made provision for an elected upper house. Independence was promised, but no date was set. The civil service in Manila was greatly Filipinised, with the number of American officials falling below 1000.

In 1921, when the Republicans regained power, General Leonard Wood was appointed Governor of the Philippines. He ran the country as though it were under martial law.

The Depression in 1930 and Japan's expansionism changed Washington's attitudes. The Hare-Hawes-Cutting Act of 1932 declared the Philippines would have self-rule from 1935 and complete independence by 1945.

Manuel Quezon, leader of the Nationalist Party, opposed the plans. His greatest concern was the termination of free trade with the United States and the continuation of American military bases within the Philippines.

The Tydings-McDuffie Independence Act passed the United States Congress in 1934. It removed the provision for military bases and established the Commonwealth of the Philippines. This was accepted by the Filipino people in May 1935. Quezon was elected President at the subsequent polls.

Japanese invasion

The progress to full independence was halted by Japan's invasion. Ten hours after the attack on Pearl Harbor in December 1941, Japanese aircraft destroyed all of the US Army Air Force in the Philippines. At the same time troops landed on Luzon and began advancing on Manila.

In 1935 Quezon had recruited retired United States General Douglas MacArthur to set up a Philippine army. MacArthur's army — eighty per cent Filipino, the rest American — was overwhelmed. They retreated to the Bataan Peninsula, west of Manila, and to Corregidor island at the entrance to Manila Bay. The plan was to hold out until reinforcements arrived.

Washington decided the Philippines was lost and diverted the reinforcements to Australia. MacArthur, ordered to abandon his troops on 11 March, was sent to Melbourne to take command of Allied forces. The defenders, who surrendered on 9 April 1942, were forced to trek 100 kilometres to a prison camp. Huge numbers died on what became known as the Bataan Death March.

Occupied

Many Filipinos conducted an insurgency war against the Japanese. The largest group was the Hukbalahap, commonly known as Huks. Led by socialists and communists, they planned to take government after the war. These guerrilla armies eventually numbered more than 250 000 members.

The landed classes accommodated themselves easily to the new imperial masters. The ordinary people, however, suffered terribly. Food became scarce, and any sign of dissent was brutally suppressed.

Governments

Manuel Quezon established a government-in-exile in Washington. In October 1944 the Japanese installed a puppet government led by former judge José Laurel. When Quezon died in August 1944, his place as president-in-exile was taken by Vice-President Sergio Osmeña.

American soldiers sent to the Philippines to take on Aguinaldo's rebels in 1899

'I Shall Return'

Stung by taunts that he had deserted the Philippines, MacArthur led a massive Allied landing at Leyte on 20 October 1944. They battled determined Japanese opposition all the way.

From 23 to 26 October 1944 the largest naval battle in history took place in the Philippine Sea. The massed Allied navy took on the Japanese fleet in a stunning engagement mostly fought by carrier-based aircraft. It left the Japanese navy crippled.

Desperate to take Manila, MacArthur pushed his forces on. The Japanese resisted violently. The American entry into Manila was slow. Their opponents fought them street by street and house by house. More than 400 000 Japanese died in a battle to the finish.

The Japanese finally surrendered on 5 July 1945. The combined ground fighting and aerial bombardment left Manila one of the most ravaged cities of World War II. More than a million Filipinos died in the fighting after the Leyte landings.

Independence

President Osmeña had landed with MacArthur's invasion force. He set up government at Tacloban on 23 October 1944 and congress met on 9 June 1945. In April 1946 Manuel Roxas of the Liberal Party defeated Osmeña to become president. The United States granted full independence on 4 July 1946.

The United States was granted 99-year leases on military establishments including Clark Field air base and Subic Bay navy base. They would play a vital part in America's involvement in the war in Vietnam.

Insurgency

Communist-led Huks began guerrilla attacks on Luzon. They regularly harassed government troops in their campaign for complete land reform until the mid-1950s. They were neutralised by a massive show of military force and a program of resettlement and land reform instituted in 1953.

Presidents and reforms

When President Roxas died in April 1948 he was replaced by Elpidio Quirino. In 1953 the newly elected President Ramón Magsaysay began a long-delayed program of land reform. His death in an air crash in March 1957 ended the ambitious plans, to the relief of large landowners

Graves at the American Cemetery in Manila of thousands of US service personnel who died in World War II

SCOTT BRODIE

US tanks patrol the bomb-devastated streets of Manila in 1945

Carolos García replaced him and went on to win a four-year term as president that same year. Next into presidential office was Diosdad Macapagal, in 1961. His greatest challenge was the nation's chronic inflation.

Economic development

As the country emerged from the devastation of war, the economy improved and industry developed. Agricultural products, which had previously dominated exports, were gradually displaced by textiles and footwear.

By the 1950s the Philippines was well ahead of its Asian neighbours economically. However, its full potential was blocked by chronic corruption in government and business. After 1954 the free trade arrangement with the United States was gradually withdrawn, ending in 1974.

The rise of Marcos

Having promised to eradicate the gun-carrying thugs who roamed the Philippines, Ferdinand Marcos was elected president in 1965. Marcos, a lawyer and regional politician, was notoriously corrupt. He had made millions by cheating the government of excise moneys on cigarettes.

Following his election, the Huks reappeared in central Luzon, assassinating officials and politicians. Moro rebels on predominantly Muslim Mindanao violently opposed the resettlement of Christians there. Marcos, having made a big show of sending in troops to quell the disturbances, became the first president to be elected for a second term in 1969.

The second term was marked by a great upsurge in violence. During 1970 there was an assassination attempt on Pope Paul VI in Manila, and demonstrators tried to break into Malacañang Palace. Violent rallies against the presence of United States bases were staged.

Martial law

Marcos was unwilling to step down as president after two terms, as required by the constitution. Using the disturbances as an excuse, he placed the country under martial law in September 1972. A new constitution greatly widened his powers. A rigged vote in 1973 gave him the right to remain president after his term expired.

In subsequent years the Philippines went from being one of the most advanced countries in South-east Asia to one of the poorest. Marcos and his business cronies plundered the nation's wealth. The millions they stole were transferred into Swiss bank accounts.

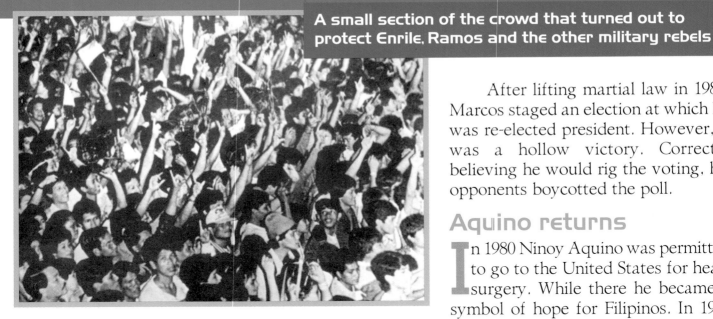

A small section of the crowd that turned out to protect Enrile, Ramos and the other military rebels

The opponents

The police and military ruthlessly suppressed dissent and rigid censorship was imposed on the media. Even so, keeping opponents quiet was not easy. The opposition was led by Senator Benigno 'Ninoy' Aquino, whom Marcos imprisoned in 1972 for eight years.

A variety of guerrilla movements kept the military tied up in constant eradication missions. The Communist Party had been revived in 1968. On the same side of politics was the New People's Army, established in 1969. On Mindanao, Muslim separatists joined the battle through their Moro National Liberation Front.

Cronyism

During the martial law period many of the country's major industries were under the control of Marcos cronies. Most were poorly run, needing huge government subsidies. The oil crisis of the mid-1970s had a dramatic effect on the economy. Interest rates rose swiftly, while prices for agricultural commodities crashed.

After lifting martial law in 1981, Marcos staged an election at which he was re-elected president. However, it was a hollow victory. Correctly believing he would rig the voting, his opponents boycotted the poll.

Aquino returns

In 1980 Ninoy Aquino was permitted to go to the United States for heart surgery. While there he became a symbol of hope for Filipinos. In 1983 Aquino returned to Manila. At the airport he was hustled off the aircraft, down to the tarmac, and shot dead. The supposed assassin was immediately killed by security officials.

Many believed Marcos ordered the killing. However, Marcos was a superb political manipulator who knew nothing would be gained from killing Aquino. It has since been speculated that his wife, Imelda Marcos, ordered the military to carry out the killing. Military Chief of Staff General Fabian Ver and twenty-five others were tried for the assassination, but all were acquitted.

Financial problems

Foreign investors withdrew their capital, fearing a total collapse of law and order. As the economy crumbled, the International Monetary Fund (IMF) agreed to bail the country out if drastic control measures were taken. As inflation soared past sixty per cent in 1984, Marcos was forced to agree to the IMF terms.

To a large extent it was the balikbayans who kept the Philippines afloat at that time. They were Filipinos working overseas as maids or construction labourers in Asian or Middle Eastern countries. In 1984 money sent home by balikbayans comprised fourteen per cent of Philippine export earnings.

Fidel Ramos

The revolution

Forced to an election in February 1986, Marco was opposed by Corazon 'Cory' Aquino, widow of the senator. Despite doing everything possible to rig the voting, the swing against him was massive. Even so, Marcos declared himself the winner.

Politicians and members of the military, including defence minister Juan Enrile and military chief General Fidel Ramos, defected to Aquino. They set up a base in a military camp where tens of thousands of civilians blocked roads, preventing tanks and Marcos-loyal troops reaching them. The end came when United States President Ronald Reagan withdrew his long-time support for Marcos.

The Marcos family was whisked from Malacañang Palace by helicopter on 25 February 1986, just as thousands of protestors were breaking down the gates. People poured into the palace to stare in awe at the evidence of the lavish Marcos lifestyle.

Marcos flew to exile in Hawaii, where he died in 1989. Imelda Marcos was charged with corruption and sentenced to eighteen years imprisonment. However, she was freed as the appeals process drags on.

President Cory

Cory Aquino was triumphantly sworn in as president. There was much goodwill for her, but she had little experience in government. Army rebels staged several coups, all put down by forces loyal to the president. She negotiated an arrangement for the United States to vacate Clark Field and Subic Bay bases in 1992. In an attempt to placate the Muslim rebels in Mindanao, a partially autonomous region was created for them.

Ferdinand and Imelda Marcos in the final days of his presidency

SCOTT BRODIE

Rizal Park in Manila, dedicated to the memory of the Philippines' greatest patriot

Solving the problems

Aquino was replaced as president by the former general, Fidel Ramos, in 1992. The most successful of all recent Philippine presidents, Ramos worked hard to revive the economy. He encouraged foreign investment and delivered much-needed stability.

Various natural disasters such as typhoons and the huge eruptions of the Mount Pinatubo volcano north of Manila had a depressing effect on economic development. One advantage was that the Philippines' slow recovery from the Marcos years meant the nation did not suffer as badly as other Asian countries in the economic collapses of 1997–98.

Erap

Stability ended in 1998 with the election of former film star Joseph 'Erap' Estrada as president. His appeal was to poorer, less well educated, voters who knew him only as a tough guy in movies.

By late 2000 it was being alleged he had links with criminal figures and had accepted huge financial pay-offs from illegal gambling operators. In January 2001 the House of Representatives and the Senate clashed over impeachment procedures. Finally, the Supreme Court removed Estrada from the presidency.

A new beginning

His replacement, on 20 January 2001, was the vice-president, Gloria Macapagal Arroyo, daughter of the president who held office prior to Marcos. Under Arroyo the nation has once more found some stability. However, the economic problems are no less daunting.

The dilemma of Muslim separatists in Mindanao continues. Following the 11 September 2001 terrorism events in the United States, they have been targeted for special attention by the American administration. United States troops were sent to the island to assist the Philippine armed forces. This move continues to cause controversy, especially with those opposed to foreign forces on Philippine soil.

www.sources

www.filipinoheritage.com/history/conflict_spain.htm
Philippine history, plus links to other sites

www.bohol.net/phillipi.htm
Concise details of Philippine history

www.infoplease.com/spot/philippinestimel.html
Timelines of Philippine history

Statistics

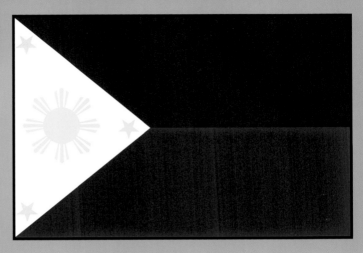

The Philippine flag was first flown in 1898. The yellow sun has eight rays, which represent the original provinces that revolted against Spanish rule. The three stars represent the major regions: Luzon, Visayas and Mindanao. In time of war the red and blue bands exchange positions.

Total population
82 850 000
Birth rate
27 per 1000 population
Death rate
6 per 1000 population
Infant mortality rate
29 per 1000 live births
Life expectancy
male 65 years
female 71 years

GDP growth rate 3.6%
GDP per capita US$3800
GDP by sector
agriculture 22%
industry 30%
services 48%

Government revenues
US$14.5 billion
Government expenditures
US$12.6 billion

Labour force 48 million
Labour force by sector
agriculture 40%
government 19%
services 18%
manufacturing 9%
construction 6%
other 8%
Unemployment rate 10%

Land area 298 170 sq. km
Lowest point
Philippine Sea — 0 m
Highest point
Mount Apu — 2954 m

Natural resources
timber, petroleum, nickel, cobalt, silver, gold, salt, copper

Primary industries
rice, coconuts, corn, sugarcane, bananas, pineapples, mangoes, pork, eggs, beef, fish
Secondary industries
textiles, pharmaceuticals, chemicals, wood products, food processing, electronics assembly, petroleum refining, fishing

Exports US$38 billion
Major exports
electronic equipment, machinery, transport equipment, garments, coconut products, labour services
Imports US$35 billion
Major imports
raw materials, intermediate goods, capital goods, consumer goods, fuels

Official languages
Pilipino, English
Currency
Philippine peso
Religions
Christianity, Islam, Buddhism

Index

Focus on Asia: Philippines   ISBN 0 86415 435 6
Published by   Franklin Watts 96 Leonard Street London EC2A4XD
Created and produced by Trocadero Publishing   Copyright © 2002 S and L Brodie   Printed in Hong Kong